# 3 Year Journal

## A Question a Day

### Lisa McGrath

Oliver Golden Publishing

# January 1

What hopes do you have for the new year?

20_____

_____

_____

_____

_____

20_____

_____

_____

_____

_____

20_____

_____

_____

_____

_____

# January 2

What did you learn in the last year?

20_____

_____

_____

_____

20_____

_____

_____

_____

20_____

_____

_____

_____

_____

# January 3

What worries are you willing to let go of today?

20_____

_____

_____

_____

_____

20_____

_____

_____

_____

20_____

_____

_____

_____

_____

# January 4

The Chinese philosopher Lao Tsu said 'the journey of a thousand miles starts with one step.' So it is with your goals. What steps can you identify that must be completed to achieve your goals?

20_____

_____

_____

_____

_____

20_____

_____

_____

_____

20_____

_____

_____

_____

_____

# January 5

Do you have a goal that gets put on a list each year, but you don't seem to do anything about it? Why?

20_____

_____

_____

_____

_____

20_____

_____

_____

_____

_____

20_____

_____

_____

_____

_____

# January 6

What do you really want from life?

20_____

_____

_____

_____

_____

20_____

_____

_____

_____

_____

20_____

_____

_____

_____

_____

# January 7

Do you take 100% responsibility for your life?

20_____

_____

_____

_____

_____

20_____

_____

_____

_____

_____

20_____

_____

_____

_____

_____

# January 8

What makes the biggest difference in your life?

20_____

_____

_____

_____

20_____

_____

_____

_____

20_____

_____

_____

_____

# January 9

How are you a work in progress?

20_____

_____

_____

_____

_____

20_____

_____

_____

_____

_____

20_____

_____

_____

_____

_____

# January 10

What did you create today?

20_____

_____

_____

_____

_____

20_____

_____

_____

_____

_____

20_____

_____

_____

_____

_____

# January 11

What has you excited to get up in the morning?

20_____

_____

_____

_____

_____

20_____

_____

_____

_____

_____

20_____

_____

_____

_____

_____

# January 12

What is present in your job that is fulfilling and full of potential?

20_____

_____

_____

_____

_____

20_____

_____

_____

_____

_____

20_____

_____

_____

_____

_____

# January 13

Are you currently thriving or surviving?

20_____
_____
_____
_____
_____

20_____
_____
_____
_____
_____

20_____
_____
_____
_____
_____

# January 14

How important are career achievements to you?

20_____
_____
_____
_____
_____

20_____
_____
_____
_____
_____

20_____
_____
_____
_____
_____

# January 15

If you died today, are you happy with the legacy you'll leave behind?

20_____

_____

_____

_____

20_____

_____

_____

_____

20_____

_____

_____

_____

# January 16

Do you have enough money to meet your current needs?

20_____

_____

_____

_____

_____

20_____

_____

_____

_____

_____

20_____

_____

_____

_____

_____

# January 17

How do you handle stress and anxiety effectively?

20_____

_____

_____

_____

_____

20_____

_____

_____

_____

20_____

_____

_____

_____

_____

# January 18

How much do you currently enjoy life outside of work or study?

20_____

_____

_____

_____

_____

20_____

_____

_____

_____

_____

20_____

_____

_____

_____

_____

# January 19

How important is managing routine tasks around the home to you?

20_____

_____

_____

_____

_____

20_____

_____

_____

_____

_____

20_____

_____

_____

_____

_____

# *January 20*

## What was the best part of today?

20_____

_____

_____

_____

20_____

_____

_____

_____

20_____

_____

_____

_____

# January 21

How do you encourage and support those closest to you?

20_____

_____

_____

_____

20_____

_____

_____

_____

20_____

_____

_____

_____

# January 22

How mentally healthy and strong do you currently feel?

20_____

_____

_____

_____

_____

20_____

_____

_____

_____

_____

20_____

_____

_____

_____

_____

# January 23

How would other people describe you?

20_____

_____

_____

_____

_____

20_____

_____

_____

_____

_____

20_____

_____

_____

_____

_____

# January 24

What can you do for hours on end and often lose track of time?

20_____

_____

_____

_____

20_____

_____

_____

_____

20_____

_____

_____

_____

# January 25

Are your current efforts going to help you achieve better life balance? If no, what needs to change?

20_____

_____

_____

_____

_____

20_____

_____

_____

_____

_____

20_____

_____

_____

_____

_____

# January 26

Define what 'success' means to you.

20_____

_____

_____

_____

_____

20_____

_____

_____

_____

_____

20_____

_____

_____

_____

_____

# January 27

Are there people you need to forgive?

20_____

_____

_____

_____

_____

20_____

_____

_____

_____

20_____

_____

_____

_____

_____

# January 28

What did you learn about yourself in the last year?

20_____

_____

_____

_____

_____

20_____

_____

_____

_____

_____

20_____

_____

_____

_____

_____

# January 29

What would your theme song be for this year?

20_____

_____

_____

_____

_____

20_____

_____

_____

_____

_____

20_____

_____

_____

_____

_____

# January 30

Has anyone had a major impact on your life in the last year?
How?

20_____

_____

_____

_____

20_____

_____

_____

_____

20_____

_____

_____

_____

# January 31

I practice self-love by _____ .

20_____

_____

_____

_____

_____

20_____

_____

_____

_____

_____

20_____

_____

_____

_____

_____

# February 1

What is present in your life partner that is fulfilling and full of potential?

20_____

_____

_____

_____

20_____

_____

_____

_____

20_____

_____

_____

_____

# February 2

Do you question your purpose, value, or worth?

20_____

_____

_____

_____

_____

20_____

_____

_____

_____

_____

20_____

_____

_____

_____

_____

# February 3

Based on your unique preferences and personality what does
your instinct tell you needs to happen for you to achieve relief
and rest for your body?

20_____

_____

_____

_____

_____

20_____

_____

_____

_____

_____

20_____

_____

_____

_____

_____

# February 4

What are the most common negative statements your negative self-talk contains? How do you reframe these statements?

20_____

_____

_____

_____

_____

20_____

_____

_____

_____

_____

20_____

_____

_____

_____

_____

# February 5

How important is being financially effective to you?

20_____

_____

_____

_____

_____

20_____

_____

_____

_____

_____

20_____

_____

_____

_____

_____

# *February 6*

What activities and commitments have you made that don't suit you?

20_____

_____

_____

_____

20_____

_____

_____

_____

20_____

_____

_____

_____

_____

# *February 7*

What do you need to give yourself permission to do, feel, or not
do?

20_____

_____

_____

_____

_____

20_____

_____

_____

_____

_____

20_____

_____

_____

_____

_____

# February 8

With whom are your closest relationships?

20_____

_____

_____

_____

_____

20_____

_____

_____

_____

_____

20_____

_____

_____

_____

_____

# February 9

What behaviors are out of alignment with your personal and professional goals?

20_____

_____

_____

_____

20_____

_____

_____

_____

20_____

_____

_____

_____

_____

# February 10

What comforts you?

20_____

_____

_____

_____

_____

20_____

_____

_____

_____

_____

20_____

_____

_____

_____

_____

# *February 11*

What do you need to give up complaining about?

20_____

_____

_____

_____

_____

20_____

_____

_____

_____

_____

20_____

_____

_____

_____

_____

# February 12

How's your commitment to your goals?

20_____

_____

_____

_____

20_____

_____

_____

_____

20_____

_____

_____

_____

_____

# *February 13*

You get more of whatever you focus on: what are you focusing on?

20_____

_____

_____

_____

20_____

_____

_____

_____

20_____

_____

_____

_____

# *February 14*

What has been a major success for you?

20_____

_____

_____

_____

_____

20_____

_____

_____

_____

_____

20_____

_____

_____

_____

_____

# *February 15*

What do you want...really, really want?

20_____

_____

_____

_____

_____

20_____

_____

_____

_____

_____

20_____

_____

_____

_____

_____

# February 16

Is there anything that you are currently procrastinating on getting done?

20_____

_____

_____

_____

_____

20_____

_____

_____

_____

_____

20_____

_____

_____

_____

_____

# *February 17*

Are you getting the most value from your life?

20_____

_____

_____

_____

_____

20_____

_____

_____

_____

_____

20_____

_____

_____

_____

_____

# February 18

Are you a list maker and a planner?

20_____

_____

_____

_____

_____

20_____

_____

_____

_____

_____

20_____

_____

_____

_____

_____

# February 19

Do you have a morning routine?

20_____

_____

_____

_____

20_____

_____

_____

_____

20_____

_____

_____

_____

# February 20

Do you have a weekly and/or monthly plan?

20_____

_____

_____

_____

_____

20_____

_____

_____

_____

_____

20_____

_____

_____

_____

_____

# *February 21*

Are there people in your life who are draining your energy and joy?

20_____

_____

_____

_____

_____

20_____

_____

_____

_____

_____

20_____

_____

_____

_____

_____

# *February 22*

Do a random act of kindness today. What did you do?

20_____

_____

_____

_____

20_____

_____

_____

_____

20_____

_____

_____

_____

# *February 23*

What are your strengths?

20_____

_____

_____

_____

_____

20_____

_____

_____

_____

_____

20_____

_____

_____

_____

_____

# February 24

What can you do for hours on end and often lose track of time?

20_____

_____

_____

_____

_____

20_____

_____

_____

_____

_____

20_____

_____

_____

_____

_____

# *February 25*

How much time do you spend focusing on yourself and your immediate needs?

20_____

_____

_____

_____

20_____

_____

_____

_____

20_____

_____

_____

_____

_____

# February 26

Are you disciplined in paying your routine household bills?

20_____

_____

_____

_____

_____

20_____

_____

_____

_____

20_____

_____

_____

_____

_____

# February 27

Are you able to do things that you enjoy frequently?

20_____

_____

_____

_____

_____

20_____

_____

_____

_____

_____

20_____

_____

_____

_____

_____

# February 28

What has been one of the most difficult lessons you've learned?

20_____

_____

_____

_____

20_____

_____

_____

_____

20_____

_____

_____

_____

# February 29

Do you sense that there's more to life and you may be missing out somehow?

20_____

_____

_____

_____

_____

20_____

_____

_____

_____

_____

20_____

_____

_____

_____

_____

# February 30

Do you have enough money to meet your current wants?

20_____

_____

_____

_____

20_____

_____

_____

_____

20_____

_____

_____

_____

# March 1

Do you find contentment and fulfillment in your current career?

20_____

_____

_____

_____

20_____

_____

_____

_____

20_____

_____

_____

_____

# March 2

How important is being generous to others to you?

20_____

_____

_____

_____

_____

20_____

_____

_____

_____

20_____

_____

_____

_____

_____

# March 3

Could you be more disciplined in managing your bills and other important responsibilities?

20_____

_____

_____

_____

_____

20_____

_____

_____

_____

_____

20_____

_____

_____

_____

_____

# March 4

What activities do you enjoy when you have free time?

20_____

_____

_____

_____

_____

20_____

_____

_____

_____

_____

20_____

_____

_____

_____

_____

# March 5

What can you do better than anyone else?

20_____

_____

_____

_____

20_____

_____

_____

_____

20_____

_____

_____

_____

# March 6

Is your self-talk positive or negative?

20_____

_____

_____

_____

_____

20_____

_____

_____

_____

_____

20_____

_____

_____

_____

_____

# March 7

How well do you communicate your ideas to others?

20_____
_____
_____
_____
_____

20_____
_____
_____
_____
_____

20_____
_____
_____
_____
_____

# March 8

Name five things you can do to work toward a larger goal you have.

20_____

_____

_____

_____

_____

20_____

_____

_____

_____

_____

20_____

_____

_____

_____

_____

# March 9

What would you like to improve about your body and why?

20_____

_____

_____

_____

_____

20_____

_____

_____

_____

_____

20_____

_____

_____

_____

_____

# March 10

What are you grateful for today?

20_____

_____

_____

_____

_____

20_____

_____

_____

_____

_____

20_____

_____

_____

_____

_____

# March 11

Who is someone that has been kind to you in your life?

20_____

_____

_____

_____

_____

20_____

_____

_____

_____

_____

20_____

_____

_____

_____

_____

# March 12

What is some of the best advice your mother ever gave you?

20_____

_____

_____

_____

20_____

_____

_____

_____

20_____

_____

_____

_____

# March 13

What would you like to re-experience again because you didn't appreciate it enough the first time?

20_____

_____

_____

_____

_____

20_____

_____

_____

_____

20_____

_____

_____

_____

_____

# March 14

What is a great mistake you have made, and why?

20_____

_____

_____

_____

_____

20_____

_____

_____

_____

20_____

_____

_____

_____

_____

# March 15

Are you a people pleaser?

20_____

_____

_____

_____

20_____

_____

_____

_____

20_____

_____

_____

_____

_____

# March 16

Do you wear perfume or cologne?

20_____

_____

_____

_____

_____

20_____

_____

_____

_____

_____

20_____

_____

_____

_____

_____

# *March 17*

Will you celebrate St. Patrick's Day?

20_____

_____

_____

_____

_____

20_____

_____

_____

_____

_____

20_____

_____

_____

_____

_____

# March 18

Think about compliments people have given you. What was your favorite one and why?

20_____

_____

_____

_____

20_____

_____

_____

_____

20_____

_____

_____

_____

# March 19

How do you plan your grocery shopping?

20_____

_____

_____

_____

20_____

_____

_____

_____

20_____

_____

_____

_____

_____

# March 20

What is the last movie that you watched?

20_____

_____

_____

_____

_____

20_____

_____

_____

_____

_____

20_____

_____

_____

_____

_____

# *March 21*

What made today special?

20_____
_____
_____
_____
_____

20_____
_____
_____
_____
_____

20_____
_____
_____
_____
_____

# March 22

What make of car do you drive, and how many miles do you have on the car?

20_____

_____

_____

_____

20_____

_____

_____

_____

20_____

_____

_____

_____

# March 23

What's the last thing you baked?

20_____
_____
_____
_____
_____

20_____
_____
_____
_____
_____

20_____
_____
_____
_____
_____

# March 24

What do you consider a luxury?

20_____

_____

_____

_____

_____

20_____

_____

_____

_____

_____

20_____

_____

_____

_____

_____

# March 25

When was your last doctor's appointment?

20_____

_____

_____

_____

20_____

_____

_____

_____

20_____

_____

_____

_____

_____

# March 26

Name three times in the past where you overcame an obstacle or in which you achieved success.

20_____

_____

_____

_____

_____

20_____

_____

_____

_____

_____

20_____

_____

_____

_____

_____

# March 27

Do you have a pet?

20_____
_____
_____
_____
_____

20_____
_____
_____
_____
_____

20_____
_____
_____
_____
_____

# March 28

How many states have you traveled to?

20_____

_____

_____

_____

_____

20_____

_____

_____

_____

_____

20_____

_____

_____

_____

_____

# March 29

Have you ever been called for jury duty?

20_____

_____

_____

_____

_____

20_____

_____

_____

_____

20_____

_____

_____

_____

_____

# March 30

Are you suffering grief that others can't understand and feel as though you must put on a brave face?

20_____

_____

_____

_____

20_____

_____

_____

_____

20_____

_____

_____

_____

# March 31

When is the last time you took public transportation?

20_____
_____
_____
_____
_____

20_____
_____
_____
_____
_____

20_____
_____
_____
_____
_____

# April 1

Is your work environment positive and supportive?

20_____

_____

_____

_____

_____

20_____

_____

_____

_____

_____

20_____

_____

_____

_____

_____

# April 2

How satisfied are you with how much you give to others?

20_____

_____

_____

_____

_____

20_____

_____

_____

_____

_____

20_____

_____

_____

_____

_____

# April 3

How important is prioritizing your responsibilities?

20_____

_____

_____

_____

_____

20_____

_____

_____

_____

_____

20_____

_____

_____

_____

_____

# April 4

How emotionally healthy and strong do you currently feel?

20_____

_____

_____

_____

_____

20_____

_____

_____

_____

_____

20_____

_____

_____

_____

_____

# April 5

What are your weaknesses?

20_____
_____
_____
_____
_____

20_____
_____
_____
_____
_____

20_____
_____
_____
_____
_____

# *April 6*

When are you most productive in your day?

20_____

_____

_____

_____

_____

20_____

_____

_____

_____

_____

20_____

_____

_____

_____

_____

# April 7

Do you enjoy speaking in front of an audience?

20_____

_____

_____

_____

_____

20_____

_____

_____

_____

_____

20_____

_____

_____

_____

_____

# April 8

Are you open to change?

20_____

_____

_____

_____

_____

20_____

_____

_____

_____

_____

20_____

_____

_____

_____

_____

# April 9

What types of rewards best motivate you?

20_____

_____

_____

_____

_____

20_____

_____

_____

_____

_____

20_____

_____

_____

_____

_____

# April 10

Do you follow your gut or intuition?

20_____

_____

_____

_____

_____

20_____

_____

_____

_____

_____

20_____

_____

_____

_____

_____

# April 11

What is one of the most romantic moments of your life?

20_____

_____

_____

_____

_____

20_____

_____

_____

_____

_____

20_____

_____

_____

_____

_____

# April 12

How did you choose which college to attend?

20_____

_____

_____

_____

_____

20_____

_____

_____

_____

_____

20_____

_____

_____

_____

_____

# April 13

What's the last thing you changed your mind about?

20_____

_____

_____

_____

_____

20_____

_____

_____

_____

_____

20_____

_____

_____

_____

_____

# April 14

What's on your mind right now?

20_____

_____

_____

_____

_____

20_____

_____

_____

_____

_____

20_____

_____

_____

_____

_____

# April 15

What's the best advice you've ever received?

20_____

_____

_____

_____

_____

20_____

_____

_____

_____

_____

20_____

_____

_____

_____

_____

# April 16

What areas of your life are working well for you?

20_____

_____

_____

_____

_____

20_____

_____

_____

_____

_____

20_____

_____

_____

_____

_____

# April 17

If you were financially secure and didn't need a salary, how would you spend your time?

20_____

_____

_____

_____

_____

20_____

_____

_____

_____

_____

20_____

_____

_____

_____

_____

# April 18

What skills or talents do you have that you are passionate about using?

20_____

_____

_____

_____

20_____

_____

_____

_____

20_____

_____

_____

_____

# April 19

Consider a previous or current job- what specific activities have you done that you enjoy and find engaging?

20_____

_____

_____

_____

_____

20_____

_____

_____

_____

_____

20_____

_____

_____

_____

_____

# April 20

What are your top five most prominent core values?

20_____

_____

_____

_____

_____

20_____

_____

_____

_____

_____

20_____

_____

_____

_____

_____

# April 21

What do you do for creative expression?

20_____

_____

_____

_____

_____

20_____

_____

_____

_____

_____

20_____

_____

_____

_____

_____

# April 22

Are you taking any medications?

20_____

_____

_____

_____

_____

20_____

_____

_____

_____

_____

20_____

_____

_____

_____

_____

# April 23

What lies are you currently telling yourself and others about who you are, what's important to you, and what you're passionate about?

20_____

_____

_____

_____

_____

20_____

_____

_____

_____

20_____

_____

_____

_____

_____

# *April 24*

What's your favorite go-to recipe?

20_____

_____

_____

_____

_____

20_____

_____

_____

_____

_____

20_____

_____

_____

_____

_____

# April 25

Are you preparing for retirement?

20_____

_____

_____

_____

_____

20_____

_____

_____

_____

_____

20_____

_____

_____

_____

_____

# April 26

What are some childhood interests or dreams you never were able to explore fully, but still find intriguing?

20_____

_____

_____

_____

_____

20_____

_____

_____

_____

_____

20_____

_____

_____

_____

_____

# April 27

What are your favorite card and board games to play?

20_____

_____

_____

_____

_____

20_____

_____

_____

_____

_____

20_____

_____

_____

_____

_____

# April 28

During an average week, how much of your time is spent doing things you dislike or that you feel waste your time?

20_____

_____

_____

_____

20_____

_____

_____

_____

20_____

_____

_____

_____

# April 29

What is the worst thing that could happen if you decided to commit fully to pursuing your passion? Could you live with this?

20_____

_____

_____

_____

_____

20_____

_____

_____

_____

20_____

_____

_____

_____

# April 30

Do you prefer the beach or the mountains?

20_____

_____

_____

_____

20_____

_____

_____

_____

20_____

_____

_____

_____

# May 1

How do you spend your weekends?

20_____

_____

_____

_____

_____

20_____

_____

_____

_____

_____

20_____

_____

_____

_____

_____

# May 2

How important is it to make charitable contributions to you?

20_____

_____

_____

_____

20_____

_____

_____

_____

20_____

_____

_____

_____

_____

# May 3

How satisfied are you with your current home environment?

20_____

_____

_____

_____

20_____

_____

_____

_____

20_____

_____

_____

_____

# May 4

Are you confident and secure in who you are as a person?

20_____

_____

_____

_____

_____

20_____

_____

_____

_____

_____

20_____

_____

_____

_____

_____

# May 5

What do you believe about yourself?

20_____

_____

_____

_____

_____

20_____

_____

_____

_____

_____

20_____

_____

_____

_____

_____

# May 6

Is the glass half empty or half full?

20_____

_____

_____

_____

20_____

_____

_____

_____

20_____

_____

_____

_____

# May 7

What's your favorite subject to talk about?

20_____

_____

_____

_____

_____

20_____

_____

_____

_____

_____

20_____

_____

_____

_____

_____

# May 8

What do you want to accomplish today?

20_____

_____

_____

_____

_____

20_____

_____

_____

_____

_____

20_____

_____

_____

_____

_____

# May 9

Do you have a garden?

20_____

_____

_____

_____

_____

20_____

_____

_____

_____

_____

20_____

_____

_____

_____

_____

# May 10

Is there anything that you are pretending to know?

20_____

_____

_____

_____

20_____

_____

_____

_____

20_____

_____

_____

_____

# May 11

Describe a favorite holiday.

20_____

_____

_____

_____

_____

20_____

_____

_____

_____

_____

20_____

_____

_____

_____

_____

# May 12

Have you lost any possessions that you were particularly fond of? What were they?

20_____

_____

_____

_____

20_____

_____

_____

_____

20_____

_____

_____

_____

# May 13

What do you wish you had spent less time worrying about?

20_____

_____

_____

_____

_____

20_____

_____

_____

_____

_____

20_____

_____

_____

_____

_____

# May 14

Do you have a lot of personal photos?

20_____
_____
_____
_____

20_____
_____
_____
_____

20_____
_____
_____
_____

# May 15

Do you need an alarm clock to wake up in the morning?

20_____

_____

_____

_____

_____

20_____

_____

_____

_____

_____

20_____

_____

_____

_____

_____

# May 16

Have you engaged in activities like drugs, alcohol, over or under-eating, or other disruptive behaviors to avoid feeling tired, stressed or anxious?

20_____

_____

_____

_____

_____

20_____

_____

_____

_____

_____

20_____

_____

_____

_____

_____

# May 17

Does your life and work currently reflect your values?

20_____

_____

_____

_____

_____

20_____

_____

_____

_____

_____

20_____

_____

_____

_____

_____

# May 18

How many hours per week do you spend checking email?
Watching TV? Surfing the Net? Social Media?

20_____

_____

_____

_____

20_____

_____

_____

_____

20_____

_____

_____

_____

_____

# May 19

What can you do to create a cushion of savings if you don't have any?

20_____

_____

_____

_____

20_____

_____

_____

_____

20_____

_____

_____

_____

# May 20

What is the last book you've read?

20_____

_____

_____

_____

_____

20_____

_____

_____

_____

20_____

_____

_____

_____

_____

# May 21

In what ways do you commonly criticize yourself?

20_____

_____

_____

_____

_____

20_____

_____

_____

_____

_____

20_____

_____

_____

_____

_____

# May 22

What activities are your biggest time wasters?

20_____

_____

_____

_____

_____

20_____

_____

_____

_____

20_____

_____

_____

_____

_____

# *May 23*

Do you have a meditation practice?

20_____

_____

_____

_____

_____

20_____

_____

_____

_____

_____

20_____

_____

_____

_____

_____

# *May 24*

What was your last vacation?

20_____

_____

_____

_____

_____

20_____

_____

_____

_____

_____

20_____

_____

_____

_____

_____

# May 25

Are you a perfectionist? In what ways?

20_____

_____

_____

_____

_____

20_____

_____

_____

_____

_____

20_____

_____

_____

_____

_____

# May 26

How do you handle stress?

20_____

_____

_____

_____

20_____

_____

_____

_____

20_____

_____

_____

_____

# May 27

How would you describe your fashion sense?

20_____

_____

_____

_____

_____

20_____

_____

_____

_____

_____

20_____

_____

_____

_____

_____

# May 28

What is something you own that is handmade?

20_____

_____

_____

_____

20_____

_____

_____

_____

20_____

_____

_____

_____

# May 29

What was the last compliment someone gave you? What was the last compliment you gave someone else?

20_____

_____

_____

_____

_____

20_____

_____

_____

_____

_____

20_____

_____

_____

_____

_____

# May 30

Name one item you can't throw away.

20_____

_____

_____

_____

_____

20_____

_____

_____

_____

_____

20_____

_____

_____

_____

_____

# May 31

Do you have a favorite restaurant?

20_____

_____

_____

_____

_____

20_____

_____

_____

_____

_____

20_____

_____

_____

_____

_____

# June 1

How important are strong working relationships to you?

20_____

_____

_____

_____

_____

20_____

_____

_____

_____

20_____

_____

_____

_____

_____

# June 2

How willing are you to step out of your comfort zone?

20_____

_____

_____

_____

_____

20_____

_____

_____

_____

20_____

_____

_____

_____

_____

# June 3

How important is dealing with home issues promptly to you?
What are you working on now?

20_____

_____

_____

_____

20_____

_____

_____

_____

20_____

_____

_____

_____

# June 4

How fulfilled are you with the way in which you're currently living your life?

20_____

_____

_____

_____

_____

20_____

_____

_____

_____

_____

20_____

_____

_____

_____

_____

# June 5

What makes you different from other people?

20_____

_____

_____

_____

20_____

_____

_____

_____

20_____

_____

_____

_____

# June 6

How do you feel around negative people?

20_____

_____

_____

_____

_____

20_____

_____

_____

_____

_____

20_____

_____

_____

_____

_____

# June 7

Do you talk to yourself?

20_____

_____

_____

_____

_____

20_____

_____

_____

_____

_____

20_____

_____

_____

_____

_____

# June 8

Are you kind to yourself?

20_____

_____

_____

_____

_____

20_____

_____

_____

_____

_____

20_____

_____

_____

_____

_____

# June 9

Under what circumstances do you ever find yourself angry?

20_____

_____

_____

_____

_____

20_____

_____

_____

_____

20_____

_____

_____

_____

_____

# *June 10*

What kinds of music do you listen to and enjoy?

20_____

_____

_____

_____

_____

20_____

_____

_____

_____

20_____

_____

_____

_____

_____

## June 11

Do you have a secret?

20_____

_____

_____

_____

_____

20_____

_____

_____

_____

_____

20_____

_____

_____

_____

_____

# June 12

Do you have a favorite teacher?

20_____

_____

_____

_____

_____

20_____

_____

_____

_____

_____

20_____

_____

_____

_____

_____

# June 13

Is there something you wish you had said to someone but didn't get the chance?

20_____

_____

_____

_____

20_____

_____

_____

_____

20_____

_____

_____

_____

# June 14

What's the last party you attended?

20_____

_____

_____

_____

_____

20_____

_____

_____

_____

20_____

_____

_____

_____

_____

# *June 15*

How do you manage stress?

20_____

_____

_____

_____

_____

20_____

_____

_____

_____

20_____

_____

_____

_____

_____

# June 16

What's your favorite sweet?

20_____

_____

_____

_____

_____

20_____

_____

_____

_____

_____

20_____

_____

_____

_____

_____

# June 17

Are there any household chores you try to avoid?

20_____

_____

_____

_____

_____

20_____

_____

_____

_____

20_____

_____

_____

_____

_____

# June 18

Is there anything in your past that you wish you could change?

20_____

_____

_____

_____

_____

20_____

_____

_____

_____

_____

20_____

_____

_____

_____

_____

# June 19

How do you check-in on the progress you are making towards your goals?

20_____

_____

_____

_____

20_____

_____

_____

_____

20_____

_____

_____

_____

# June 20

How many unopened emails do you have?

20_____

_____

_____

_____

_____

20_____

_____

_____

_____

_____

20_____

_____

_____

_____

_____

# June 21

Do you have a favorite piece of jewelry?

20_____

_____

_____

_____

_____

20_____

_____

_____

_____

20_____

_____

_____

_____

# June 22

Do you have a favorite television show?

20_____

_____

_____

_____

_____

20_____

_____

_____

_____

_____

20_____

_____

_____

_____

_____

# June 23

If you could go back in time and change something, what would it be?

20_____

_____

_____

_____

_____

20_____

_____

_____

_____

_____

20_____

_____

_____

_____

_____

# June 24

Describe the last hat you wore.

20_____

_____

_____

_____

_____

20_____

_____

_____

_____

_____

20_____

_____

_____

_____

_____

# June 25

How much money do you have on hand?

20_____

_____

_____

_____

20_____

_____

_____

_____

20_____

_____

_____

_____

_____

# June 26

What are your favorite shoes?

20_____
_____
_____
_____
_____

20_____
_____
_____
_____
_____

20_____
_____
_____
_____
_____

# June 27

On a scale of one to ten, how healthy are you?

20_____

_____

_____

_____

_____

20_____

_____

_____

_____

_____

20_____

_____

_____

_____

_____

# June 28

Have you reviewed your top 3 goals? List your milestones and achievements.

20_____

_____

_____

_____

_____

20_____

_____

_____

_____

20_____

_____

_____

_____

_____

# June 29

What's the last zoo or amusement park you went to?

20_____
_____
_____
_____
_____

20_____
_____
_____
_____
_____

20_____
_____
_____
_____
_____

# June 30

Do you have a unique talent?

20_____

_____

_____

_____

_____

20_____

_____

_____

_____

_____

20_____

_____

_____

_____

_____

# July 1

What's in your refrigerator?

20_____

_____

_____

_____

_____

20_____

_____

_____

_____

_____

20_____

_____

_____

_____

_____

# July 2

How much do you worry about your current financial situation?

20_____

_____

_____

_____

_____

20_____

_____

_____

_____

20_____

_____

_____

_____

_____

# July 3

Would your home life be easier if you had a better system in place for managing your routine responsibilities? How?

20_____

_____

_____

_____

20_____

_____

_____

_____

20_____

_____

_____

_____

# *July 4*

How spiritually healthy do you currently feel?

20_____

_____

_____

_____

_____

20_____

_____

_____

_____

_____

20_____

_____

_____

_____

_____

# July 5

If you were on a sports team, what contribution would you make?

20_____

_____

_____

_____

_____

20_____

_____

_____

_____

_____

20_____

_____

_____

_____

_____

# July 6

What motivates you?

20_____

_____

_____

_____

_____

20_____

_____

_____

_____

_____

20_____

_____

_____

_____

_____

# July 7

What's your preferred style of communication: verbal or nonverbal?

20_____

_____

_____

_____

_____

20_____

_____

_____

_____

_____

20_____

_____

_____

_____

_____

# July 8

Do you reward yourself when you accomplish tasks?

20_____

_____

_____

_____

_____

20_____

_____

_____

_____

_____

20_____

_____

_____

_____

_____

# July 9

What results would you like to achieve?

20_____

_____

_____

_____

_____

20_____

_____

_____

_____

_____

20_____

_____

_____

_____

_____

# July 10

What's your favorite question to ask people?

20_____

_____

_____

_____

_____

20_____

_____

_____

_____

_____

20_____

_____

_____

_____

_____

# July 11

Are you more like your mother or father? In what ways?

20_____

_____

_____

_____

_____

20_____

_____

_____

_____

_____

20_____

_____

_____

_____

_____

# July 12

What was it like to learn how to drive? Are you a good driver?

20_____

_____

_____

_____

_____

20_____

_____

_____

_____

_____

20_____

_____

_____

_____

_____

# July 13

What choice are you thankful that you did not make?

20_____

_____

_____

_____

_____

20_____

_____

_____

_____

_____

20_____

_____

_____

_____

_____

# *July 14*

What's a funny story people tell about you?

20_____

_____

_____

_____

_____

20_____

_____

_____

_____

_____

20_____

_____

_____

_____

_____

# July 15

What is a problem you solved today?

20_____

_____

_____

_____

_____

20_____

_____

_____

_____

_____

20_____

_____

_____

_____

_____

# July 16

What's your biggest indulgence?

20_____

_____

_____

_____

_____

20_____

_____

_____

_____

_____

20_____

_____

_____

_____

_____

# July 17

What memberships have you joined?

20_____
_____
_____
_____
_____

20_____
_____
_____
_____
_____

20_____
_____
_____
_____
_____

# July 18

Have you found yourself questioning your values, beliefs, or religion?

20_____

_____

_____

_____

_____

20_____

_____

_____

_____

_____

20_____

_____

_____

_____

_____

# July 19

What would it take for you to be debt-free?

20_____

_____

_____

_____

_____

20_____

_____

_____

_____

_____

20_____

_____

_____

_____

_____

# July 20

When was the last time you had some ice cream?

20_____

_____

_____

_____

_____

20_____

_____

_____

_____

20_____

_____

_____

_____

_____

# July 21

Have you ever judged someone for declining an invitation
when you didn't think they had a good reason?

20_____

_____

_____

_____

_____

20_____

_____

_____

_____

20_____

_____

_____

_____

_____

# July 22

When's the last time you had a belly laugh?

20_____

_____

_____

_____

_____

20_____

_____

_____

_____

_____

20_____

_____

_____

_____

_____

# July 23

When's the last time you were on an elevator?

20_____

_____

_____

_____

_____

20_____

_____

_____

_____

_____

20_____

_____

_____

_____

_____

# July 24

Do you have a favorite quote?

20_____

_____

_____

_____

_____

20_____

_____

_____

_____

_____

20_____

_____

_____

_____

_____

# July 25

What's the last park you visited?

20_____

_____

_____

_____

_____

20_____

_____

_____

_____

_____

20_____

_____

_____

_____

_____

# July 26

What do you consider to be your biggest achievement?

20_____

_____

_____

_____

_____

20_____

_____

_____

_____

_____

20_____

_____

_____

_____

_____

# Jul 27

Do you wear a watch?

20_____

_____

_____

_____

_____

20_____

_____

_____

_____

_____

20_____

_____

_____

_____

_____

# July 28

What do you do with your spare change?

20_____

_____

_____

_____

_____

20_____

_____

_____

_____

_____

20_____

_____

_____

_____

_____

# July 29

If you had the chance to start fresh all over again with your life, your relationships, and your career, what would you do differently?

20_____

_____

_____

_____

_____

20_____

_____

_____

_____

20_____

_____

_____

_____

_____

# July 30

What's the last gift you received?

20_____

_____

_____

_____

_____

20_____

_____

_____

_____

20_____

_____

_____

_____

_____

# July 31

What's the last museum you visited?

20_____

_____

_____

_____

_____

20_____

_____

_____

_____

_____

20_____

_____

_____

_____

_____

# August 1

Do you have a healthy and rewarding work/life balance?

20_____

_____

_____

_____

_____

20_____

_____

_____

_____

_____

20_____

_____

_____

_____

_____

# August 2

How important is establishing personal and professional boundaries to you?

20_____

_____

_____

_____

_____

20_____

_____

_____

_____

20_____

_____

_____

_____

# August 3

How much do you worry about your routine responsibilities?

20_____

_____

_____

_____

_____

20_____

_____

_____

_____

_____

20_____

_____

_____

_____

_____

# August 4

Are you authentic in your life both inside and out?

20_____

_____

_____

_____

_____

20_____

_____

_____

_____

_____

20_____

_____

_____

_____

_____

# August 5

What, if anything, are you settling for in your life?

20_____

_____

_____

_____

_____

20_____

_____

_____

_____

_____

20_____

_____

_____

_____

_____

# August 6

What keeps you going?

20_____

_____

_____

_____

_____

20_____

_____

_____

_____

_____

20_____

_____

_____

_____

_____

# August 7

Are you a good listener?

20_____

_____

_____

_____

_____

20_____

_____

_____

_____

_____

20_____

_____

_____

_____

_____

# August 8

What is your normal work week?

20_____
_____
_____
_____
_____

20_____
_____
_____
_____
_____

20_____
_____
_____
_____
_____

# August 9

How would you describe your childhood?

20_____
_____
_____
_____
_____

20_____
_____
_____
_____
_____

20_____
_____
_____
_____
_____

# *August 10*

## Who has been your closest friend?

20_____

_____

_____

_____

20_____

_____

_____

_____

20_____

_____

_____

_____

# *August 11*

What do you miss most about being a child?

20_____

_____

_____

_____

20_____

_____

_____

_____

20_____

_____

_____

_____

# August 12

How would you describe your faith?

20_____
_____
_____
_____
_____

20_____
_____
_____
_____
_____

20_____
_____
_____
_____
_____

# August 13

What is your favorite snack?

20_____

_____

_____

_____

_____

20_____

_____

_____

_____

_____

20_____

_____

_____

_____

_____

# August 14

What bothered you today?

20_____

_____

_____

_____

_____

20_____

_____

_____

_____

20_____

_____

_____

_____

# August 15

If you could meet anyone, alive or dead, who would it be, and why?

20_____

_____

_____

_____

_____

20_____

_____

_____

_____

20_____

_____

_____

_____

# August 16

How ambitious do you feel today?

20_____

_____

_____

_____

_____

20_____

_____

_____

_____

_____

20_____

_____

_____

_____

_____

# *August 17*

What details from today would you like to remember?

20_____

_____

_____

_____

_____

20_____

_____

_____

_____

_____

20_____

_____

_____

_____

_____

# *August 18*

When's the last time you had a good cry?

20_____

_____

_____

_____

_____

20_____

_____

_____

_____

20_____

_____

_____

_____

_____

# August 19

Do you have any tattoos?

20_____
_____
_____
_____
_____

20_____
_____
_____
_____

20_____
_____
_____
_____
_____

# August 20

On a scale of one to ten, how spontaneous were you today?

20_____

_____

_____

_____

20_____

_____

_____

_____

20_____

_____

_____

_____

# August 21

What's your favorite outfit?

20_____

_____

_____

_____

_____

20_____

_____

_____

_____

_____

20_____

_____

_____

_____

_____

# August 22

What's your favorite comfort food?

20_____

_____

_____

_____

_____

20_____

_____

_____

_____

_____

20_____

_____

_____

_____

_____

# August 23

Have you ever been on television or the radio?

20_____

_____

_____

_____

20_____

_____

_____

_____

20_____

_____

_____

_____

# August 24

Are you in debt? Can you develop a plan to become debt-free?

20_____

_____

_____

_____

_____

20_____

_____

_____

_____

_____

20_____

_____

_____

_____

_____

# August 25

What plan can you make to spruce up your workspace to make it feel more joyful?

20_____

_____

_____

_____

_____

20_____

_____

_____

_____

20_____

_____

_____

_____

# August 26

Who is the last person you talked with on your cell phone?

20_____

_____

_____

_____

20_____

_____

_____

_____

20_____

_____

_____

_____

# August 27

What countries have you traveled to?

20_____

_____

_____

_____

_____

20_____

_____

_____

_____

_____

20_____

_____

_____

_____

_____

# August 28

What's something interesting about you that most people may not know?

20_____

_____

_____

_____

_____

20_____

_____

_____

_____

_____

20_____

_____

_____

_____

_____

# August 29

What's been one of your biggest challenges?

20_____

_____

_____

_____

_____

20_____

_____

_____

_____

_____

20_____

_____

_____

_____

_____

# *August 30*

What's your favorite conversation starter?

20_____

_____

_____

_____

_____

20_____

_____

_____

_____

_____

20_____

_____

_____

_____

_____

# *August 31*

What's a life lesson that's benefitted you?

20_____

_____

_____

_____

_____

20_____

_____

_____

_____

_____

20_____

_____

_____

_____

_____

# September 1

Does your career stimulate and develop you as a person?

20_____

_____

_____

_____

_____

20_____

_____

_____

_____

_____

20_____

_____

_____

_____

_____

# September 2

How important is your physical health to you?

20_____
_____
_____
_____
_____

20_____
_____
_____
_____
_____

20_____
_____
_____
_____
_____

# September 3

How much easier would your life be if you were more disciplined in managing your routine responsibilities around the home?

20_____

_____

_____

_____

20_____

_____

_____

_____

20_____

_____

_____

_____

# September 4

How consistent are you at managing your emotions?

20_____

_____

_____

_____

_____

20_____

_____

_____

_____

_____

20_____

_____

_____

_____

_____

# September 5

What are you denying about yourself or your life?

20_____

_____

_____

_____

_____

20_____

_____

_____

_____

_____

20_____

_____

_____

_____

_____

# September 6

Do you find yourself worrying when your mind is idle?

20_____

_____

_____

_____

_____

20_____

_____

_____

_____

_____

20_____

_____

_____

_____

_____

# September 7

What change do you need to make in how you see the world?

20_____

_____

_____

_____

_____

20_____

_____

_____

_____

_____

20_____

_____

_____

_____

_____

# September 8

Life is good, could it be better?

20_____

_____

_____

_____

_____

20_____

_____

_____

_____

_____

20_____

_____

_____

_____

_____

# September 9

Do you handle rejection well?

20_____

_____

_____

_____

_____

20_____

_____

_____

_____

_____

20_____

_____

_____

_____

_____

# September 10

What gives you peace of mind?

20_____

_____

_____

_____

_____

20_____

_____

_____

_____

_____

20_____

_____

_____

_____

_____

# September 11

Where were you during 9/11? What do you remember?

20_____

_____

_____

_____

_____

20_____

_____

_____

_____

_____

20_____

_____

_____

_____

_____

# September 12

What is something that you have won?

20_____

_____

_____

_____

_____

20_____

_____

_____

_____

_____

20_____

_____

_____

_____

_____

# September 13

Describe a cherished memory.

20_____

_____

_____

_____

_____

20_____

_____

_____

_____

_____

20_____

_____

_____

_____

_____

# September 14

What is preventing you from pursuing your primary passion in life?

20_____

_____

_____

_____

_____

20_____

_____

_____

_____

_____

20_____

_____

_____

_____

_____

# September 15

How could today have been better?

20_____

_____

_____

_____

20_____

_____

_____

_____

20_____

_____

_____

_____

# September 16

What's your favorite outdoor activity?

20_____
_____
_____
_____
_____

20_____
_____
_____
_____
_____

20_____
_____
_____
_____
_____

# September 17

What limiting beliefs or fears have held you back from finding
or pursuing your main passion in the past?

20_____

_____

_____

_____

20_____

_____

_____

_____

20_____

_____

_____

_____

# September 18

What's on your to-do list?

20_____

_____

_____

_____

_____

20_____

_____

_____

_____

_____

20_____

_____

_____

_____

_____

# September 19

How do you practice self-care?

20_____

_____

_____

_____

_____

20_____

_____

_____

_____

_____

20_____

_____

_____

_____

_____

# September 20

In what way's are you frugal?

20_____

_____

_____

_____

_____

20_____

_____

_____

_____

_____

20_____

_____

_____

_____

_____

# September 21

What do you try to avoid?

20_____
_____
_____
_____
_____

20_____
_____
_____
_____
_____

20_____
_____
_____
_____
_____

# September 22

What do you love about your life?

20_____

_____

_____

_____

_____

20_____

_____

_____

_____

_____

20_____

_____

_____

_____

_____

# September 23

What did you get done today?

20_____

_____

_____

_____

_____

20_____

_____

_____

_____

20_____

_____

_____

_____

# September 24

What is your personal motto?

20_____

_____

_____

_____

_____

20_____

_____

_____

_____

_____

20_____

_____

_____

_____

_____

# September 25

What's a new habit you want to adopt?

20_____

_____

_____

_____

20_____

_____

_____

_____

20_____

_____

_____

_____

# September 26

Do you have a gratitude practice?

20_____

_____

_____

_____

_____

20_____

_____

_____

_____

_____

20_____

_____

_____

_____

_____

# September 27

What's unique about you?

20_____

_____

_____

_____

_____

20_____

_____

_____

_____

_____

20_____

_____

_____

_____

_____

# September 28

List three things that made you smile today.

20_____

_____

_____

_____

20_____

_____

_____

_____

20_____

_____

_____

_____

# September 29

What's an area of your life that you would like to improve?

20_____

_____

_____

_____

20_____

_____

_____

_____

20_____

_____

_____

_____

# September 30

What is one positive change you have already made this year?

20_____

_____

_____

_____

_____

20_____

_____

_____

_____

_____

20_____

_____

_____

_____

_____

# October 1

How much do you look forward to going to work each day?

20_____

_____

_____

_____

20_____

_____

_____

_____

20_____

_____

_____

_____

# October 2

How happy are you with your current physical fitness levels?

20_____

_____

_____

_____

_____

20_____

_____

_____

_____

_____

20_____

_____

_____

_____

_____

# October 3

How important is contributing back to society and making a difference to you?

20_____

_____

_____

_____

_____

20_____

_____

_____

_____

_____

20_____

_____

_____

_____

_____

# October 4

What are the main challenges (or difficulties) that you're currently facing in life?

20_____

_____

_____

_____

_____

20_____

_____

_____

_____

20_____

_____

_____

_____

_____

# October 5

What is keeping you stuck?

20_____

_____

_____

_____

_____

20_____

_____

_____

_____

_____

20_____

_____

_____

_____

_____

# October 6

What is it to be passionate? What are you passionate about?

20_____

_____

_____

_____

_____

20_____

_____

_____

_____

_____

20_____

_____

_____

_____

_____

# October 7

Are you always honest with yourself?

20_____

_____

_____

_____

_____

20_____

_____

_____

_____

20_____

_____

_____

_____

_____

# October 8

How well do you focus at work?

20_____

_____

_____

_____

_____

20_____

_____

_____

_____

_____

20_____

_____

_____

_____

_____

# October 9

What progress have you made on your goals?

20_____
_____
_____
_____
_____

20_____
_____
_____
_____
_____

20_____
_____
_____
_____
_____

# October 10

What are your favorite memories of your children growing up?

20_____

_____

_____

_____

_____

20_____

_____

_____

_____

_____

20_____

_____

_____

_____

_____

# October 11

What's the strangest thing that has ever happened to you?

20_____

_____

_____

_____

_____

20_____

_____

_____

_____

_____

20_____

_____

_____

_____

_____

# October 12

Describe a magical experience.

20_____

_____

_____

_____

_____

20_____

_____

_____

_____

_____

20_____

_____

_____

_____

_____

# October 13

What are you most proud of?

20_____

_____

_____

_____

_____

20_____

_____

_____

_____

_____

20_____

_____

_____

_____

_____

# October 14

When's the last time you rode a bike?

20_____

_____

_____

_____

_____

20_____

_____

_____

_____

_____

20_____

_____

_____

_____

_____

# October 15

How did you send your day?

20_____

_____

_____

_____

_____

20_____

_____

_____

_____

_____

20_____

_____

_____

_____

_____

# October 16

If you could have a superpower just for today, what would it be?

20_____

_____

_____

_____

_____

20_____

_____

_____

_____

20_____

_____

_____

_____

_____

# October 17

What's your favorite thing to do on a rainy day?

20_____

_____

_____

_____

_____

20_____

_____

_____

_____

_____

20_____

_____

_____

_____

_____

# October 18

What was in your mailbox today?

20_____

_____

_____

_____

_____

20_____

_____

_____

_____

20_____

_____

_____

_____

# October 19

Do you have an accountability partner?

20_____

_____

_____

_____

_____

20_____

_____

_____

_____

20_____

_____

_____

_____

_____

# October 20

What is a decision you made today?

20_____

_____

_____

_____

_____

20_____

_____

_____

_____

_____

20_____

_____

_____

_____

_____

# October 21

What's in your car glove compartment?

20_____

_____

_____

_____

_____

20_____

_____

_____

_____

_____

20_____

_____

_____

_____

_____

# October 22

What is the most important thing you should accomplish in the next 24 hours?

20_____

_____

_____

_____

_____

20_____

_____

_____

_____

_____

20_____

_____

_____

_____

_____

# October 23

When's the last time you took a nap?

20_____

_____

_____

_____

_____

20_____

_____

_____

_____

20_____

_____

_____

_____

# October 24

What new activity have you tried?

20_____
_____
_____
_____
_____

20_____
_____
_____
_____

20_____
_____
_____
_____

# October 25

How do you want to be remembered?

20_____

_____

_____

_____

_____

20_____

_____

_____

_____

_____

20_____

_____

_____

_____

_____

# October 26

If you could change one thing about today, what would it be?

20_____

_____

_____

_____

20_____

_____

_____

_____

20_____

_____

_____

_____

# October 27

How many steps do you average per day?

20_____

_____

_____

_____

_____

20_____

_____

_____

_____

_____

20_____

_____

_____

_____

_____

# October 28

What question(s) do you hate to answer?

20_____

_____

_____

_____

_____

20_____

_____

_____

_____

_____

20_____

_____

_____

_____

_____

# October 29

How do you make big decisions in your life?

20_____

_____

_____

_____

_____

20_____

_____

_____

_____

_____

20_____

_____

_____

_____

_____

# October 30

In three words, describe your day.

20_____

_____

_____

_____

_____

20_____

_____

_____

_____

_____

20_____

_____

_____

_____

_____

# October 31

What could you talking about for 60 minutes without preparation?

20_____

_____

_____

_____

_____

20_____

_____

_____

_____

_____

20_____

_____

_____

_____

_____

# November 1

How fulfilled are you in your current work environment?

20_____

_____

_____

_____

_____

20_____

_____

_____

_____

_____

20_____

_____

_____

_____

_____

# November 2

How content are you with the amount of free time you have?

20_____

_____

_____

_____

20_____

_____

_____

_____

20_____

_____

_____

_____

# November 3

How do you regularly make a positive impact in the lives of other people?

20_____

_____

_____

_____

_____

20_____

_____

_____

_____

_____

20_____

_____

_____

_____

_____

# November 4

What is working really well in your life at this stage of your life?

20_____

_____

_____

_____

_____

20_____

_____

_____

_____

20_____

_____

_____

_____

_____

# November 5

What past hurts and sufferings do you need to let go?
Acknowledge what you have learned along the way.

20_____

_____

_____

_____

_____

20_____

_____

_____

_____

20_____

_____

_____

_____

_____

# November 6

What actions are you avoiding?

20_____

_____

_____

_____

_____

20_____

_____

_____

_____

_____

20_____

_____

_____

_____

_____

# November 7

How do you let go of fear when you are in a challenging situation?

20_____

_____

_____

_____

_____

20_____

_____

_____

_____

_____

20_____

_____

_____

_____

_____

# November 8

Do you have any unfinished tasks/projects?

20_____

_____

_____

_____

20_____

_____

_____

_____

20_____

_____

_____

_____

# November 9

What's a lesson you learned this week?

20_____

_____

_____

_____

20_____

_____

_____

_____

20_____

_____

_____

_____

# November 10

What qualities do you most value in a friend?

20_____

_____

_____

_____

20_____

_____

_____

_____

20_____

_____

_____

_____

# November 11

Do you have anyone close to you that has served in the military?

20_____

_____

_____

_____

_____

20_____

_____

_____

_____

_____

20_____

_____

_____

_____

_____

# November 12

Who is the wisest person you know?

20_____

_____

_____

_____

20_____

_____

_____

_____

20_____

_____

_____

_____

# November 13

Do you have any memorable stories about family members?

20_____

_____

_____

_____

_____

20_____

_____

_____

_____

_____

20_____

_____

_____

_____

_____

# November 14

What is your next big step working towards your goals?

20_____

_____

_____

_____

20_____

_____

_____

_____

20_____

_____

_____

_____

_____

# November 15

What did you do for physical activity today?

20_____

_____

_____

_____

20_____

_____

_____

_____

20_____

_____

_____

_____

# November 16

How do you get out of a rut?

20_____

_____

_____

_____

_____

20_____

_____

_____

_____

_____

20_____

_____

_____

_____

_____

# November 17

What is something you keep on your nightstand?

20_____

_____

_____

_____

_____

20_____

_____

_____

_____

_____

20_____

_____

_____

_____

_____

# November 18

What is something you have that has improved the quality of your life?

20_____

_____

_____

_____

_____

20_____

_____

_____

_____

_____

20_____

_____

_____

_____

_____

# November 19

When's the last time you went on a picnic?

20_____

_____

_____

_____

_____

20_____

_____

_____

_____

_____

20_____

_____

_____

_____

_____

# November 20

How do you show others that you appreciate them?

20_____

_____

_____

_____

20_____

_____

_____

_____

20_____

_____

_____

_____

# November 21

What's an unforgettable experience you've had?

20_____

_____

_____

_____

_____

20_____

_____

_____

_____

_____

20_____

_____

_____

_____

_____

# November 22

Do you have a favorite breakfast?

20_____

_____

_____

_____

_____

20_____

_____

_____

_____

_____

20_____

_____

_____

_____

_____

# November 23

What's the longest car trip you've taken this year?

20_____

_____

_____

_____

_____

20_____

_____

_____

_____

20_____

_____

_____

_____

# November 24

How do you prioritize your time?

20_____

_____

_____

_____

20_____

_____

_____

_____

20_____

_____

_____

_____

# November 25

When's the last time you went to the beach?

20_____

_____

_____

_____

_____

20_____

_____

_____

_____

20_____

_____

_____

_____

_____

# November 26

What are you grateful for today?

20_____

_____

_____

_____

20_____

_____

_____

_____

20_____

_____

_____

_____

# November 27

When is the last time you had an inspiring conversation?

20_____

_____

_____

_____

20_____

_____

_____

_____

20_____

_____

_____

_____

# November 28

What's the last thing you sent out in the mail?

20_____

_____

_____

_____

_____

20_____

_____

_____

_____

20_____

_____

_____

_____

_____

# November 29

What does the following quote mean to you? "The most powerful relationship you will ever have is the relationship with yourself". –Steve Maraboli

20_____

_____

_____

_____

_____

20_____

_____

_____

_____

_____

20_____

_____

_____

_____

_____

# November 30

Write a positive affirmation for yourself.

20_____

_____

_____

_____

_____

20_____

_____

_____

_____

_____

20_____

_____

_____

_____

_____

# December 1

How satisfying are your career achievements to date?

20_____

_____

_____

_____

_____

20_____

_____

_____

_____

_____

20_____

_____

_____

_____

_____

# December 2

How satisfied are you with your current physical appearance?

20_____

_____

_____

_____

_____

20_____

_____

_____

_____

_____

20_____

_____

_____

_____

_____

# December 3

How important is leaving behind a meaningful legacy to you?

20_____

_____

_____

_____

_____

20_____

_____

_____

_____

20_____

_____

_____

_____

_____

# December 4

What would it take for your life to feel more effectively balanced?

20_____

_____

_____

_____

_____

20_____

_____

_____

_____

_____

20_____

_____

_____

_____

_____

# December 5

What expectations do you have for yourself and your life?

20_____

_____

_____

_____

_____

20_____

_____

_____

_____

_____

20_____

_____

_____

_____

_____

# December 6

What is your attention on today?

20_____

_____

_____

_____

_____

20_____

_____

_____

_____

20_____

_____

_____

_____

# December 7

How do you see the people you work with? How do they see you?

20_____

_____

_____

_____

_____

20_____

_____

_____

_____

_____

20_____

_____

_____

_____

_____

# December 8

What are three words to describe your social life?

20_____

_____

_____

_____

_____

20_____

_____

_____

_____

_____

20_____

_____

_____

_____

_____

# *December 9*

What personal and professional goals do you want to set for
the coming new year?


20_____

_____

_____

_____

_____

20_____

_____

_____

_____

20_____

_____

_____

_____

_____

# December 10

Did you ever have car trouble at a particularly inconvenient time?

20_____

_____

_____

_____

_____

20_____

_____

_____

_____

_____

20_____

_____

_____

_____

_____

# December 11

What do you think about space travel?

20_____

_____

_____

_____

_____

20_____

_____

_____

_____

20_____

_____

_____

_____

_____

# December 12

What is something that most people would be surprised to know about you?

20_____

_____

_____

_____

20_____

_____

_____

_____

20_____

_____

_____

_____

# December 13

What is something unusual that you own?

20_____

_____

_____

_____

_____

20_____

_____

_____

_____

_____

20_____

_____

_____

_____

_____

# December 14

Where do you go for good ideas?

20_____

_____

_____

_____

_____

20_____

_____

_____

_____

_____

20_____

_____

_____

_____

_____

# December 15

What's the last item you purchased?

20_____

_____

_____

_____

_____

20_____

_____

_____

_____

20_____

_____

_____

_____

_____

# December 16

What technology do you use on a regular basis?

20_____

_____

_____

_____

_____

20_____

_____

_____

_____

_____

20_____

_____

_____

_____

_____

# December 17

Where do you see yourself in five years?

20_____

_____

_____

_____

_____

20_____

_____

_____

_____

_____

20_____

_____

_____

_____

_____

# December 18

What's the last check you wrote?

20_____

_____

_____

_____

20_____

_____

_____

_____

20_____

_____

_____

_____

# December 19

Do you have holiday traditions? Any favorites?

20_____

_____

_____

_____

_____

20_____

_____

_____

_____

_____

20_____

_____

_____

_____

_____

# December 20

Are you a risk taker? What's the last risk you took?

20_____

_____

_____

_____

20_____

_____

_____

_____

20_____

_____

_____

_____

# December 21

What's on your wish list?

20_____
_____
_____
_____
_____

20_____
_____
_____
_____

20_____
_____
_____
_____
_____

# December 22

When's the last time you had your haircut?

20_____

_____

_____

_____

_____

20_____

_____

_____

_____

_____

20_____

_____

_____

_____

_____

# December 24

How often do you check social media?

20_____

_____

_____

_____

_____

20_____

_____

_____

_____

_____

20_____

_____

_____

_____

_____

# December 25

What are you sentimental about?

20_____

_____

_____

_____

_____

20_____

_____

_____

_____

_____

20_____

_____

_____

_____

_____

# December 26

What's one word that captures how you want to feel next year?

20_____

_____

_____

_____

_____

20_____

_____

_____

_____

_____

20_____

_____

_____

_____

_____

# December 27

What's the last souvenir you purchased?

20_____

_____

_____

_____

_____

20_____

_____

_____

_____

20_____

_____

_____

_____

# December 28

Have you created a Vision Board for next year?

20_____

_____

_____

_____

_____

20_____

_____

_____

_____

20_____

_____

_____

_____

# *December 29*

What's the last picture on your phone?

20_____

_____

_____

_____

_____

20_____

_____

_____

_____

_____

20_____

_____

_____

_____

_____

# December 30

Write a phrase to describe your year.

20_____

_____

_____

_____

_____

20_____

_____

_____

_____

20_____

_____

_____

_____

_____

# December 31

What is your most cherished memory of this year?

20_____

_____

_____

_____

_____

20_____

_____

_____

_____

_____

20_____

_____

_____

_____

_____

Meet Lisa McGrath, Achievement Coach...international bestselling author, speaker, teacher, and coach. Lisa's search for a deeper meaning and purpose began as a little girl because she was thrust into adulthood early. She lived on her own and sought out ways of living a more meaningful life. A spiritual calling led her on a journey of healing and purpose.

International Best-Selling Author, Speaker, and Coach
Lisa McGrath

She learned that we ALL have stories, but sometimes we don't feel like we have a voice. As an Achievement

Coach, she helps others, especially entrepreneurs, coaches, and aspiring authors like herself, craft their stories that help heal, inspire, and support others. Participants in her Writing, Publishing, and Marketing course have the opportunity to submit their stories for the international bestselling anthology Pages with Purpose that helps the authors gain visibility, authority, and credibility.

Made in the USA
Monee, IL
27 April 2022

95521934R00203